DEVON

Halswood

ADDRESS BOOK

Published by Halswood Stationers

British Library Cataloguing-in-Publication Data
A CIP record for this title is available
from the British Library

ISBN 978 0 85717 002 6

HALSWOOD STATIONERS
Halsgrove House,
Ryelands Industrial Estate,
Bagley Road, Wellington, Somerset TA21 9PZ
Tel: 01823 653777   Fax: 01823 216796
email: sales@halsgrove.com

Part of the Halsgrove group of companies
Information on all Halsgrove titles is available at:
www.halsgrove.com

Printed and bound in China by
Toppan Leefung Printing Ltd (010)

Front cover: Sunset walk, Torrington. **David Elliot**

Back cover: Looking across the estuary to Salcombe.
Lee Pengelly

Title page: Appledore Cottages. **David Elliot**

Right: Hope Cove Cottages, South Hams.
Jeremy Willcocks

Overleaf: Wallabrook Bridge, Dartmoor.
Jeremy Willcocks

YOUR ADDRESS BOOK

Since the invention of the camera in the mid nineteenth century, photographers have found inspiration in the Devon landscape. Today, with digital cameras so widely available, almost everyone has an opportunity to capture mementos of a favourite place, or a chance event. But not all of us have the skill, or patience, to wait for that single moment when all the conditions fall into place and the perfect image is captured.

Like many of us, the photographers whose work appears in this address book, have fallen for the beauty and variety of scenery that the county has to offer. From dramatic seascapes and sweeping moorland vistas, to impressive townscapes and tiny hamlets, each has been able to find a scene or scenery to arrest their interest. However, their skills usually far surpass those of us who happily snap away in order to record a moment. Their photography comes at a price, often with years of training and experience in the best use of complex and expensive equipment, with early starts and endless hours waiting for the right moment, and above all with an artist's eye in knowing what will make a good photograph.

These photographers are part of a long tradition of those who have been inspired to capture the elusive qualities of light, atmosphere and character that make Devon so special. Their work has been selected to portray something of the variety and range of contemporary photography being created today. Each in their own distinctive way, captures the essence of the place. They have been chosen as they are among the best known in the county and most have their homes here. Information about each can be found at the end of this book.

Address books tend to be well used and have a long life. Along with important contact details, they keep track of the user's friends and acquaintances, tracing their lives over time and from place to place. And, if properly attended to, an address book eventually becomes a journal in itself, and an attractive and permanent keepsake.

Whether you have bought this book for your own use, or receive it as a gift, we hope this *Devon Address Book,* with its superb pictorial reminders of Devon, provides years of pleasure.

USEFUL ADDRESSES AND TELEPHONE NUMBERS

A

Looking across the estuary to Salcombe.
Lee Pengelly

A

Cottages at Buckland-in-the-Moor.
Adrian Oakes

B

Black-a-tor Copse, Dartmoor.
Jen Bryant

B

B

B

Lynmouth, North Devon.
Jason Hawkes

C

Smeaton's Tower, Plymouth Hoe.
Lee Pengelly

C

C

C

Ancient Dartmoor clapper bridge at Scorhill.
Adrian Oakes

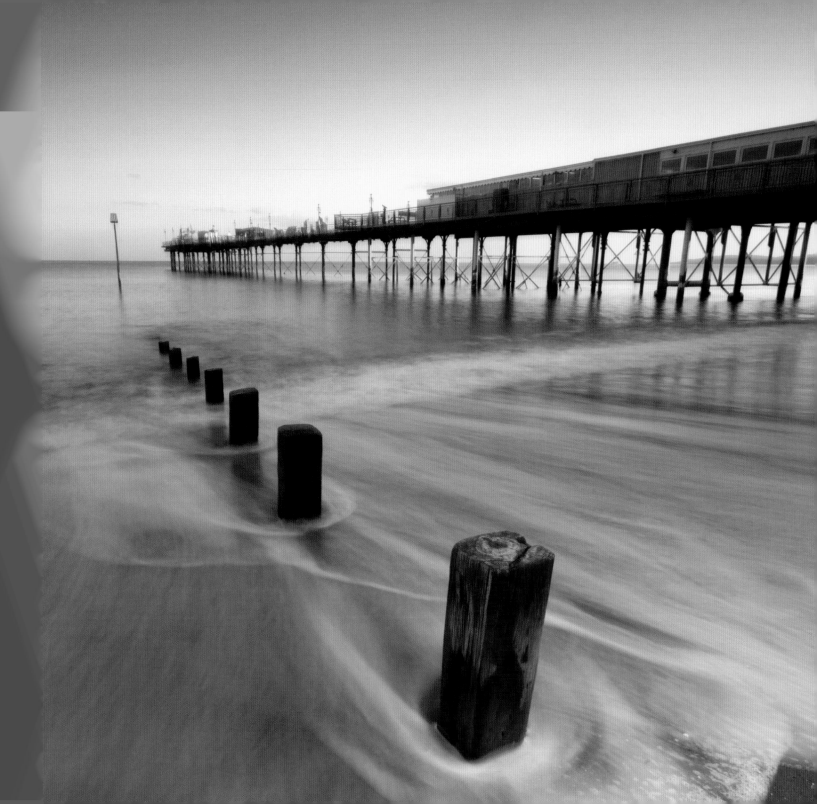

D

The pier, Teignmouth.
Lee Pengelly

D

D

D

Out of the mist, Salcombe.
Jeremy Willcocks

E

Wheal Betsy, Dartmoor.
Adrian Oakes

E

E

E

Beach huts at Budleigh Salterton.
Carol Ballenger

F

Kinsgwear.
Jason Hawkes

F

F

F

Exeter Cathedral, evening.
Lee Pengelly

G

Dawn on Exmouth Esplanade.
Lee Pengelly

G

G

G

Sunset Walk, Torrington.
David Elliot

H

Brentor church.
Adrian Oakes

H

H

H

Fishing Boats, North Devon
David Elliott

Torquay harbour, early morning.
Lee Pengelly

I

Stormy skies near Aveton-Gifford.
Jeremy Willcocks

J

Looking across Holwell Tor with Haytor beyond.
Jen Bryant

J

Ilfracombe harbour
Jason Hawkes

K

_____   _____
_____   _____
_____   _____
_____   _____
_____   _____
_____   _____
_____   _____
_____   _____
_____   _____
_____   _____
_____   _____
_____   _____
_____   _____
_____   _____
_____   _____
_____   _____
_____   _____
_____   _____
_____   _____
_____   _____

Hartland storm.
Jeremy Willcocks

K

Coombe Martin at dusk.
Lee Pengelly

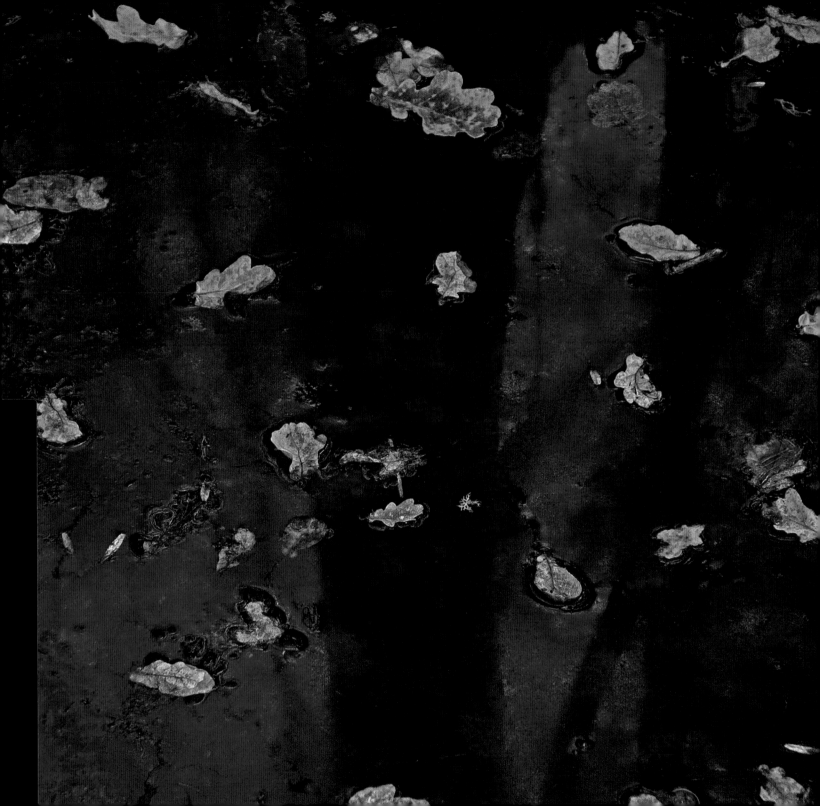

L

Ice Pool, Dartmoor.
Carol Ballenger

L

L

L

Clovelly.
Jeremy Willcocks

Dartmoor Ponies at Merrivale.
Jen Bryant

M

M

M

Dawn light on the Exeter canal.
Lee Pengelly

N

N

_____

_____

_____

_____

_____

_____

_____

_____

_____

_____

_____

_____

_____

_____

_____

_____

The Barbican, Plymouth.
Lee Pengelly

N

Winter near Kings Tor, Dartmoor
Adrian Oakes

O

o

East Dart Waterfall.
Jeremy Willcocks

O

A peaceful morning on the Yealm Estuary at Newton Ferrers.
Jen Bryant

PQ

Lustleigh.
Jeremy Willcocks

Red sandstone at Dawlish.
Lee Pengelly

R

Dawn at Bideford Bridge.
David Elliott

S

S

Clovelly.
Jason Hawkes

S

S

S

Saltram House.
Lee Pengelly

T

Saddle Tor, Dartmoor.
Adrian Oakes

T

T

The pier at Torquay harbour.
Lee Pengelly

UV

_____
_____
_____
_____
_____
_____
_____
_____
_____
_____
_____
_____
_____
_____
_____
_____
_____

Storm at Hartland Quay
David Elliott

UV

The waterfall on Hoar Oak Water above Watersmeet.
Jen Bryant

W

Summer on Dartmoor, near Foggintor.
Carol Ballenger

W

Roundham Head.
Jason Hawkes

A lone tree near Black Tor, Dartmoor.
Adrian Oakes

XYZ

ABOUT THE PHOTOGRAPHERS

Carol Ballenger works in the landscape, both rural and urban, and produces archival quality, signed, limited edition photographs in her studio. She has exhibited widely and is a member of the Devon Guild of Craftsmen and a Fellow of the Royal Photographic Society. Her books Dartmoor Dreams and Stone Universe are published by Halsgrove. As a musician and founder of Arts Live, Carol promotes various projects including live performances combining projected images, poetry and music. Contact details: www.artslive.org.uk. email: carol.ballenger@artslive.org.uk.

Jen Bryant combines her passion for photography with her love of walking, starting her career in photography with black and white images before turning predominantly to colour. As with so many professionals she appreciates the need for early starts in order to get the best light, or to take advantage of the low sun that evenings often provide. Her first book *Perfect Devon* is published by Halsgrove. Contact details: www.jenbryant.co.uk. email: jensphotography@googlemail.com.

David Elliott is relatively new to professional photography but since retirement has established a company which produces and supplies a range of photographic products including high quality greeting cards, mounted photographic prints, and canvases. Due to the increasing demand he is now exploring having images published more widely, combining this with a passion for travel. Contact details: www.northdevonphotography.co.uk. email: elliott.photos@btinternet.com.

Jason Hawkes is one of the country's best-known photographers specialising in aerial photography. From his base near London he travels worldwide to produce images for books, advertising and design. Since 1991 he has provided photographs for major international companies including Nike, HSBC, Ford, Rolex, Toyota and BP. Among over twenty books he has published with Halsgrove and others are the superb aerial photography books *North Devon Coast from the Air*; and *South Devon Coast from the Air*. Contact details: www.jasonhawkes.com. email: library@jasonhawkes.com.

Adrian Oakes is a landscape and contemporary photographer based in Devon. He has kindled a great love and respect for Dartmoor over the last twenty years and more recently has focused on photographing its diverse landscapes and rich history. His clients include The Dartmoor National Park Authority and the National Trust who also sell prints and cards of his work. Adrian specialises in panoramas of Dartmoor and East Devon and has had photographs published in a variety of media including *Devon Life* magazine and in promotional material for Canonteign Falls. His books Perfect Dartmoor and Dartmoor: A Winter's Tale are published by Halsgrove. Forthcoming is a book based on his Dartmoor panoramic images. Contact details: www.adrianoakes.com. email: akoblackbird@hotmail.com.

Lee Pengelly was born in Plymouth in 1970 and lives and works in Devon. He picked up his first camera in his early twenties and became instantly hooked with photography. In order to develop his skills, Lee studied a two-year course with the Bureau of Freelance Photographers, which also provided him with an understanding of the commercial side of the business and covered all the aspects of marketing his work. Using 35mm, medium and large format equipment he now supplies work to picture libraries, magazines, books, postcard and calender companies and local businesses. His books with Halsgrove include *Devon's Beautiful Buildings*, and *Devon Moods, A Portrait of Exeter* and *A Portrait of Plymouth*. Contact: www.silverscenephoto.co.uk. email: Leepengelly@aol.com.

Jeremy Willcocks lives in the South Hams where the landscape provides constant inspiration for photography, his principal passion. As a member of the Royal Photographic Society, he achieved one of his goals in 2006 by gaining a Licentiateship in photography, granting him the letters LRPS after his name. He has sold pieces of his work to the Dartmoor National Park and in galleries in the South West. As well as selling prints, he also sells greetings cards, and calendars. Contact details: www.southwestscenes.me.uk. email: Southwestscenes1@aol.com.